A newspaper report

Read this newspaper report and answer the questions below.

Young boy saves family from house fire in Madison County

A.J. Rollins, 11, says he woke up early Wednesday morning and noticed smoke and flames in his family's home on Will Arrington Road in Marshall. "I woke up and it was right in front of me," A.J. said. "I just ran through the hallways and started waking everybody up."

A.J. says the fire grew bigger as the family rushed to get out. "Just big flames everywhere," he told us.

The home is destroyed, but A.J.'s parents say they consider their family lucky. "I don't believe anyone would have survived if it hadn't been for A.J. waking up," said Dwayne Rollins, A. J.'s father.

The Arrington Branch Baptist Church in Marshall is collecting donations to help get the family back on their feet.

I. Write an alternative headline for the report. _____

2. Write brief comments from two other people that could be included in the report. For example: *Next door neighbour, Celia Rawlings said, 'I thought I smelled burning, but just assumed my husband had burned the toast, but as the smell became stronger I realised something very serious was happening ...'*

Comments from a first person that could be included	Comments from a second person that could be included

3. List three differences between a newspaper report and a diary.

Newspaper report	Diary

Meaning and spelling of connectives

 1 Match a connective to its purpose.

> to sum up, so, for instance, also, so far, furthermore, in conclusion, in particular, such as, alternatively, secondly, overall, next, in addition, for example, as well as, in summary, again, therefore, nevertheless, consequently, as a result, however, but, on the other hand, firstly, meanwhile, in fact, importantly

Purpose of connectives	Connective
Adding on information	*also*
Giving examples	
Changing/contrasting ideas	
Ordering ideas	
Emphasising ideas	
Summing up points	

2 Use these connectives in sentences of your own. You will need to write more than one sentence to show that you can link and connect points:

as a result	furthermore	on the other hand	to sum up

For example, *We won the football game. **As a result,** we have come top of the school league.*

a _____

b _____

c _____

d _____

3 Write out instructions on how to wash your hands. How many connectives can you use?

_____

_____

_____

_____

_____

Complex sentences

1 Circle the main clause and underline the subordinate clause in these sentences.

   a Mateo did not go to school because he was ill.

   b Zara said she enjoyed doing mathematics, although she finds it difficult.

   c Despite being well behaved, Teresa was told off by the teacher.

   d Although she had not revised as much as she should, Aaliyah got top marks in the English examination.

   e We will have to stay inside if it rains all day.

   f I was soon completely lost because I had forgotten the map.

   g They continued to hunt for survivors until it was dark.

   h I walked home when it was light.

   i We would have gone for a picnic if the weather had been fine.

2 Re-write each of the sentences above so that they begin with a subordinate clause. You will need to use a comma to mark it off from the rest of the sentence. The first one has been done for you.

   a *Because he was ill, Mateo did not go to school.*

   b _____

   c _____

   d _____

   e _____

   f _____

   g _____

   h _____

   i _____

3 Complete these complex sentences so that you explain or describe what is happening at that moment. They all begin with a non-finite clause. Remember to add a comma to mark off the clause. The first one has been done for you:

   a *Waving his arms wildly, the man ran out of the house.*

   b Running fast _____ .

   c Grabbing the driving wheel _____ .

   d Surprised by what he had seen _____ .

   e Tiptoeing cautiously _____ .

   f Watched by his family and friends _____ .

5

More complex sentences

1 Underline the verb in each of the sentences below.

a The boy kicked the football along the street.

b The angry child stamped her foot on the path.

c The large boy grabbed Ian by the arm.

d Owls have good eyesight.

e The girl hurried towards school.

2 Start each of the above sentences with a non-finite form of the verb, and add additional information. Remember to use a comma to mark off the non-finite clause. The first one has been done for you.

a *Kicking the ball along the street, the boy made his way home.*

b _____

c _____

d _____

e _____

3 Insert the four missing commas in this newspaper report.

Why it's Not Cool to Be Cool

Do you ever feel frustrated that you're not one of the coolest kids at your school?

If you do don't worry because you may be better off!

Researchers have found that the less cool kids at school (and children who find it more of a challenge to fit in) are often more successful in later life compared to the more popular kids.

After following 184 teenagers for ten years researchers at the University of Virginia found that by the age of 23 the less cool or geeky kids were more successful in terms of social skills. By being too focused on being cool cool kids would seem to lose out in later life!

Features of a newspaper report

 Read this newspaper article about a new theme park.

Star turn: world gets first sports theme park

If you've ever wondered what it's like to run a 100 metre sprint alongside Usain Bolt or ride in the **peloton** in the Tour de France, you will be able to find out at Open Camp, the world's first sports theme park. 7000 visitors a day are expected to visit the theme park when it opens in Barcelona next year.

Simulators and other forms of interactive technology will give visitors the thrill of being a downhill skier or a top football player. There will even be award ceremonies with flags and podiums. 'We will film it using cameras and drones and a full production team so that you can relive the experience on television at home,' the organisers say.

Every night between June and September there will be a full scale closing ceremony with winners mounting the podium to receive their medals.

The park, covering an area of 95,000 sq. metres, will be on Montjuic, a hill near the city centre. It will use the Olympic stadium and other facilities built for the 1992 Olympic games. The upgrade will cost 20 million Euros (£15.8 m); it is expected to create 240 jobs and bring an estimated £53 million to the city.

A full price ticket of £45 allows you to participate in a game of football or basketball, run a 1500 metre race or take part in an Olympic discipline. The basic entrance fee will be £28, similar to most theme parks. Tickets will go on sale via a mobile app that will also serve as a guide to the theme park.

Francesc Medina, the plan's promoter, has coined the term 'sportainment' for the park, emphasising that 'it is for everyone'. They expect 7000 visitors a day to take part in the 56 activities on offer.

Word bank

peloton: riding together as a pack/group
simulator: a machine designed to provide a realistic imitation of something

 Answer the following questions.

a Why does the headline include the phrase, 'star turn'?

_____

b Underline two quotations in the report which best explain why the theme park is called Open Camp.

c Circle the paragraph that gives the summary of the story: 1 2 3 4 5 6

d Give three pieces of evidence from the text which shows that Open Camp is technologically advanced.

_____

_____

_____

e How is Open Camp able to offer a skiing experience?

_____

Presenting a newspaper report

1 Read the newspaper report on page 7 again. Give three reasons why visitors might want to go to Open Camp.

_____

_____

_____

2 Imagine you have been asked to present 'Open Camp' as part of the television news. You only have a **30** second slot, so will need to select the most essential information (the facts).

Use the following table to select key information.

What is Open Camp?	
Where is it being built?	
Why is it special?	
Who is it for?	
How much did it cost?	
When is it opening?	
Promoter comments	

3 Write your report here. Remember, the slot is only **30** seconds long.

_____

_____

_____

_____

_____

_____

_____

_____

Tips

You will need to ensure that:

- all the key information is included
- key words and phrases are underlined, to help you remember to emphasise these a little more
- you don't just read from your notes. Remember to look at the 'audience' now and again!
- you read at the right pace and don't mumble.

Writing a newspaper report

Write a newspaper report about a new type of theme park opening in the area where you live. This theme park could be focused on: performance; swimming/diving; skateboarding; cycling; cricket; football; netball. The theme should be something you know about.

Use the table below to help you plan your newspaper article about the new theme park.

Headline	
What is the theme park called?	
What is the theme?	
Special features	
Where is it being built ?	
Size/expected visitors	
How much did it cost to build?	
When is it opening?	
Comments from people	
Positive vocabulary	For example, *thrilling, latest film techniques*

Writing a newspaper report

Use the table below to help you structure your report.

First paragraph: overview of the story (hint: use the opening paragraph from 'Star turn' on page 7 as a model).
Some detail about what, who, where, when, why.
A comment from someone about the theme park – perhaps a planner, organiser or builder.
Some more detail about what, who, where, when, why.
A comment from someone else – perhaps a visitor or someone who is thinking of going to the theme park.
Finish off with a reference to the future.

Writing a newspaper report

1 Write your completed newspaper report here.

Self-assessment

Unit 1

Looking closer at non-fiction

 I understand this well

 I understand this but need more practice

😞 I don't understand this

Learning Objectives	☺	😐	😞
Phonics, spelling and vocabulary			
I know the meanings and spellings of connectives.			
Grammar and punctuation			
I can point out the main clause and subordinate clause in a complex sentence.			
I can use connectives to structure an argument or discussion.			
I can use punctuation such as commas, to mark out the meaning in complex sentences.			
Reading: Non-fiction			
I can recognise the key features of a newspaper report.			
I can describe how paragraphs are structured and linked in a newspaper report.			
Writing: Non-fiction			
I can write a newspaper report using the features of this text type.			
I can summarise a passage.			
I know the difference between fact and opinion.			
Speaking and listening			
I can prepare, practise and improve a spoken presentation.			

_____

_____

_____

_____

 I need more help with ...

Biography, autobiography and diaries

Charles Dickens

 Read this short biography of Charles Dickens, the famous English writer. Underline any words you are unsure of, and look these up in a dictionary.

Charles Dickens (7 February 1812–9 June 1870) was an English writer who created some of the world's most memorable fictional characters and is generally regarded as the greatest novelist of the Victorian period. Even today his books are widely read and studied in schools.

Born in Portsmouth, England, Charles Dickens was forced to leave school at the age of nine and start work in a blacking factory (a boot polish factory) after his father was jailed for having bad debts. He worked there for three years: the conditions were very poor and he suffered from acute loneliness. However, this early impoverishment drove him on to succeed. In 1833 he was employed as the parliamentary reporter for *The Morning Chronicle* newspaper and in 1836, his first novel, *The Pickwick Papers* was published. This proved to be very popular and Dickens started to become famous. His novels were published in monthly parts, so each month people could read a new chapter. Perhaps this is why Dickens' books make good films and TV serials! Dickens lived through the Industrial Revolution, and in his stories wrote about how life was changing, especially for poor people. Indeed, many poor people (who were often illiterate) paid their half penny to have each new monthly episode read to them, so opening up and inspiring a new class of readers.

Charles Dickens went on to produce a massive amount of material during his lifetime. He published fifteen novels, wrote hundreds of short stories and non-fiction pieces, lectured and performed both in England and in the United States, wrote plays, wrote thousands of letters and edited two journals. His 1843 novella, *A Christmas Carol*, is regarded as one of the most influential works ever written, and his 1859 novel, *A Tale of Two Cities*, is the bestselling novel of all time.

On his death in 1870 at the age of 58, Charles Dickens was buried in Poet's Corner of Westminster Abbey – a site still visited by thousands of people every year.

Meaning of words you are unsure of:

Biography

 Read the short biography on page 13 again and answer these questions.

1. Explain why each of these dates are important in the life of Charles Dickens.

1812	
1836	
1843	
1859	
1870	

2. What information is **missing** from this biography of Charles Dickens?

_____

_____

_____

3. Give one word from the text which means being unable to read or write.

_____

4. Using the information from the biography on page 13, create an 'Interesting fact file' on Charles Dickens. At least six facts are required. You could carry out some research and find out some more facts about his life and work, and add these.

Charles Dickens Fact File

_____

_____

_____

_____

_____

_____

_____

_____

_____

_____

Shades of meaning in words

 Read the biography on page 13 again and answer these questions.

1. Give two pieces of evidence from the text that show Charles Dickens worked hard during his lifetime.

   _____

   _____

2. Give two opinions from the text.

   _____

   _____

3. Write out the meaning of the words underlined so that they mean the same.

   a   he suffered from <u>acute</u> loneliness

   _____

   b   Charles Dickens went on to produce a <u>massive</u> amount of material during his lifetime.

   _____

4. Match these synonyms with the correct meaning.

anger	the feeling of being upset because of being unable to achieve something
frustration	strong feeling of annoyance
fury	the feeling of being impatient or slightly angry
irritation	extreme sometimes violent anger

5. Put these synonyms in order from the least to the most. Use a dictionary to help you.

   a hungry, ravenous, peckish: _____

   b exhausted, weary, sleepy: _____

   c giggle, guffaw, chuckle: _____

   d dash, jog, sprint: _____

   e stride, stroll, toddle: _____

Autobiography

 Read these extracts from two very different autobiographies and answer the questions on page 17.

Extract 1

Extract 2

Usain Bolt (1986 –) is a Jamaican field and track athlete. He is considered the fastest person ever, holding both the 100m and 200m world records and is the first man to win six Olympic gold medals in sprinting. His achievements have earned him the nickname 'Lightning Bolt'. In this extract from his autobiography 'Faster than Lightning: My Story' he recalls his early experiences at primary school.

'At school I was pretty good in class, especially math, and when lessons began I made an important discovery: man, I loved to compete! As soon as a problem went up on the chalk board, I'd race to finish. Often NJ would battle me to see who could complete the sums first, and that's when the killer instinct showed up. Everything I got involved in, I did it to win. I *had* to win. First was everything, second only meant losing. And I really hated losing.

I cruised through my first few years at school, and sports quickly became my thing. Thanks to all that running around the wild bush in Coxheath I was fast.'

Jessica Ennis (1986 –) is a field and track athlete from Sheffield, England. She won a gold medal at the London Olympics in 2012 for the heptathlon. In this extract from her autobiography 'Jessica Ennis: Unbelievable – From My Childhood Dreams to Winning Olympic Gold' the reader finds out about both the past and present.

'I am crying. I am a Sheffield schoolgirl writing in her diary about the bullies awaiting me tomorrow. They stand menacingly by the gates and lurk unseen in my head, mocking my size and status. They make a small girl shrink, and I feel insecure and frightened.

I pour the feelings out into words on the page, as if exposing them in some way will help, but nobody sees my diary.

Fast forward two decades and I am crying again. I am standing in a cavernous arena in London.

Suddenly, the pain and suffering and frustration give way to a flood of overwhelming emotion. In the middle of this enormous arena I feel smaller than ever, but I puff out my chest, look to the flag and stand tall. It has been a long and winding road from the streets of Sheffield to the tunnel that feeds into the Olympic Stadium…'

Comparing two autobiographies

Read the extracts on page 16 and answer these questions.

1 The questions below refer to both extracts.

   a Underline the words and phrases which tell you about the writers' feelings.

   b Underline the words and phrases which describe where the writers are.

   c Give three similarities between the two extracts and three differences.

   i _____

   _____

   ii _____

   _____

   iii _____

   _____

2 Which extract do you prefer and why?

I prefer _____

because _____

_____

3 Write a three to four sentence description of your earliest memory in the style of either *My Story* or *Unbelievable*.

_____

_____

_____

_____

_____

_____

_____

_____

Prefixes

1 Use the prefixes **auto, circum, trans** to complete these words.
Use a dictionary to help you.

a _____matic   b _____form

c _____psy   d _____vent

e _____plant   f _____navigate

g _____port   h _____mit

2 bi = two or twice   tri = three   oct = eight

What are the answers?

a bike with three wheels	
sea creature with eight tentacles	
a bike with two wheels	
a shape with eight sides	
a plane with two wings	
a three legged stand	
eighth tone in a musical scale	
occurring every two years	
a figure with three sides and three angles	

3 'Inter' means among or between; 'micro' means small. Add the correct prefix to the root words below.

wave   act   view   sect   city   scope   chip   circuit   fere   national

4 Give three words beginning with each of these word roots. Use a dictionary to help you!

geo – earth	
dict – say	
hydra – water	
man – hand	
vit – life	

Suffixes

1 Add suffixes to these words. Take care with spelling.

a beauty + ful _____

b cycle + ist _____

c happy + ness _____

d study + ent _____

e wise + dom _____

f argue + ment _____

2 Take the suffixes off each word. Write the root word correctly.

a icicle _____

b service _____

c loveable _____

d mountaineer _____

e explosion _____

f sparkle _____

3 Change these nouns into verbs by adding **en**, **ify** or **ise**.

a drama _____

b tight _____

c solid _____

d advert _____

e simple _____

4 Write two synonyms for each of the following words. Ensure that the word class stays the same.

a help (verb) _____ _____

b friend (noun) _____ _____

c difficult (adjective) _____ _____

d brave (adjective) _____ _____

e tried (verb) _____ _____

f fear (noun) _____ _____

Word origins and definitions

American English

Americans speak English because that was the language of most of the settlers, the best known of whom were called the Pilgrim Fathers. They sailed from Plymouth in England to America in 1620 onboard a ship called the 'Mayflower'.

Americans use different words from English for some things. For example, the English say 'tap' while the Americans say 'faucet'.

1   Draw lines to match the following American words with the English equivalents.

chips	autumn
sidewalk	sweets
elevator	biscuit
fall	case
candy	lift
cookie	crisps
yard	garden
trunk	pavement

2   Write the opposite of these words by using a prefix

a correct _____   f content _____

b obey _____   g polite _____

c selfish _____   h direct _____

d advantage_____   i order _____

e patient _____   j pure _____

3   These words came from Greece. Write down what they mean.

a theatre _____

b orchestra _____

c chorus _____

d alphabet _____

Diaries

1 From the list below, underline five features typical of diary texts.

> written in the first person; written in the second person; written in the third person; recounts what has happened; describes feelings; formal style; chatty style; treats all events in the same way; mostly in the present tense; mostly in the past tense; meant to be widely read.

2 Read this diary entry from *The Wreck of the Zanzibar* by Michael Morpurgo. Laura's twin brother, Billy has decided to run away to sea to escape the harsh conditions on Bryher, a very tiny island where the family are finding it very hard to make a living.

'I'm going, Laura,' Billy said. 'I was thinking about it all last night. And not just because of Father, either. It's a big world out there and I'm going to see it. This could be my only chance.'

And I could see that he meant it, that I couldn't argue him round. I tried all the same. I begged him to stay. I even said I'd go with him. He shook his head and looked away. I know Billy so well, better than he knows me, I think. Once he's made up his mind there's no stopping him. I knew it was hopeless.

He put his arm around me and told me he was sorry, that I'd be all right. He'd write to me, and when he comes back he's going to bring me lots of things from America, from China, from the frozen North. When I cried he hugged me very tight and said he'd go now, just as he was. He didn't want to have to go home again.

'You'll tell Mother?' he said. 'You'll say goodbye for me?'

I walked in silence with him down past the church to the quay. We saw Father paring a hedge up in the field where Molly had died. Billy looked at him and said nothing. He was close to tears. He turned away.

'And say goodbye to 'Granny May' too,' he said. From the quayside we looked across at St Mary's. We could see the masts of the 'General Lee'.

'She's a fine ship,' he said. 'A fast ship. She'll take me all over the world, Joseph Hannibal said.'

He smoothed my hair and told me to go home without looking back. I cried all the way home, not so much because Billy was gone and I might never see him again, but because he didn't want me to go with him.

This evening, from the top of Samson Hill, I watched the 'General Lee' sail out past St Agnes. Billy was right. She was a fine ship. I knew he'd be looking back at Bryher and he knew I'd be up on Samson Hill. I could feel his eyes on me. I shivered, not from cold, but because I knew then as I know now, that I'll never see Billy again. Her sails were red in the last of the sun, as red as any blood.

a Underline the use of the first person.

b Underline references to feelings and emotions.

3 What do you think is going to happen next?

Writing a diary extract

 Turn the following extract into a short diary entry written by James. This should focus on his feelings. Remember to write in the first person.

A board has appeared outside James's house with some mysterious writing on it. Helen, his sister, has invited a friend, Julia, back home for tea.

Helen and her friend, a pale girl with plaits, were already seated at the table. They watched him come in with a disapproving stare.

Mrs Harrison asked, 'What are you girls planning to do after tea?'

They exchanged looks and began to giggle. 'We'll tell you later, ' said Helen in a heavy whisper. James arranged his face in what he hoped was an expression of deep, sneering contempt. That was one of the many things about girls, the business of going all secret and ridiculous and pretending they were up to something. He sighed deeply and stared out of the window with the preoccupied look of someone who has real concerns.

'That board,' said Helen, 'We thought it was you. We thought it was silly.'

James closed his eyes and assumed an expression of tired **resignation**...

Word bank

resignation:
the acceptance of something not particularly wanted but seen as inevitable

2 Write the diary entry here.

_____

_____

_____

_____

_____

_____

_____

_____

Self-assessment

Unit 2

Biography, autobiography and diaries

😊	I understand this well
😐	I understand this but need more practice
☹️	I don't understand this

Learning Objectives	😊	😐	☹️
Phonics, spelling and vocabulary			
I know how to transform the meaning of a word with a prefix or a suffix.			
I can talk about shades of meaning in words.			
I can point out the root of a word and explain its origin.			
Grammar and punctuation			
I know what language features to use when writing a diary.			
I can change a word class using a suffix.			
Reading: Non-fiction			
I understand the features of autobiography and biography texts.			
I can compare the language features of two different autobiographies.			
I can recognise key characteristics of a diary text.			
I know about first and third person narration.			
Writing: Non-fiction			
I can adapt the features and style of a diary text in my own writing.			
I know how to write an autobiography and what features to use.			
Speaking and listening			
I can express and explain my ideas clearly.			
I can speak confidently in a formal situation.			

I need more help with ...

_____

_____

_____

_____

23

Reports and argument

Non-chronological reports

 A non-chronological report will organise information for the reader. Here is some information about the whale. Indicate where a new paragraph would start and then write down a suitable heading for each paragraph. This will let the reader know what the paragraph is going to be about.

The whale is the common name for various marine mammals of the order *Cetacea*, and includes the sperm whale, killer whale, pilot whale and beluga whale. It excludes dolphins and porpoises, as these belong to the suborder *Odontoceti* (toothed whales). Whales range in size from the blue whale, the largest animal known to have ever existed at 30 m (98 ft) in length and weighing 180 tonnes to the pygmy species such as the pygmy sperm whale at 3.5 m (11 ft). Like all mammals, whales breathe air, are warm-blooded, nurse their young with milk from mammary glands, and have body hair. Beneath the skin lies a layer of fat called blubber, which stores energy and insulates the body. Whales breathe via blowholes; baleen whales have two and toothed whales have one. These are located on the top of the head, allowing the animal to remain almost completely submerged while breathing. Breathing involves expelling stale air, followed by inhaling fresh air into the lungs. Whales inhabit all the world's oceans and number in the millions. Whales are long-lived, with humpback whales living for up to 77 years, while bowhead whales may live for over a century. Human hunting of whales from the 17th century until 1986 radically reduced the populations of some whale species.

Paragraph 1 heading _____

Paragraph 2 heading _____

Paragraph 3 heading _____

Paragraph 4 heading _____

Paragraph 5 heading _____

Non-chronological reports

2 Read the text on page 24 again and answer these questions.

a Why are dolphins and porpoises not included in the main order of whales, the *Cetacea*?

_____

b This is an information text, with many technical and scientific terms used.
Write down four.

_____

_____

_____

_____

c Sometimes, information is presented as interesting facts. Which four facts would you choose?

_____

_____

_____

d The words *suborder* and *submerged* are used. Other words using the prefix *sub* are *submarine, substandard*. What do you think the prefix 'sub' means?

_____

3 Information texts like the one on page 24 will often use the passive voice.

> A verb is passive when the subject of the sentence has the action done to it.
> For example, *The boy slammed the door.*
> A verb is active when the subject of the sentence performs the sentence.
> For example, *The door was slammed by the boy.*

Decide whether each of these sentences is in the active or passive voice, by writing A or P next to each one.

a The field was ploughed by the farmer. _____
b The teacher read a story to the class. _____
c The football player hit the ball with his foot. _____
d The new dress was worn by the young girl. _____
e I spent a lot of money on chocolate. _____
f A car was driven by the old man. _____

4 On another piece of paper, change these sentences from active to passive.

a My sister asked me to go home for the weekend. (I was ...)
b My mother picked me up from the station. (I was ...)
c My father cleaned the kitchen. (The kitchen ...)
d Gideon broke the vase. (The vase ...)
e The ambulance took the sick girl to hospital. (The sick girl ...)

Report on a controversial issue

Read this report about the destruction of Nigeria's forests, then answer the questions which follow.

Forests

Nigeria's forests once covered large areas of the country. Today they cover only around 10 per cent of the total land area. Forest products are widely used by around 90 per cent of the rural population for fuel wood, food products, timber, construction materials and local medicines. Population growth and rising oil fuel prices have placed great pressure on the forests as people turn to wood as an alternative fuel. Experts believe that if current rates of deforestation continue then all of Nigeria's forests could be gone by 2020. The government is now launching various action plans to protect and conserve the forests. It is also encouraging tree planting to increase forest coverage.

Gabriel is a conservation officer at Okomu National Park in Edo State. He says 'At one time, this area was covered in thick forest, but today our park contains the last rainforest in southwest

Nigeria. It is a very important park and home to many endangered species. We monitor poaching by local people who use the forest to hunt for bush meat. We realise that people depend on the forest for their livelihoods, but it is in everybody's interest to manage the forest wisely. Finding the balance between local needs and conservation remains a great challenge!'

a What us the main reason suggested by the report for the deforestation of Nigeria?

b What do the rural population use forest products for?

c Figures have been used in the report to demonstrate the severity of the problem. Can you underline the words or phrases which suggest these figures are not exact?

d Why is deforestation a controversial issue in Nigeria?

e Is the report written in an emotive tone or an impersonal tone?

f What is your opinion? What do you think could be done to protect the forest and the needs of the rural population? Will you write your response in an emotive tone or an impersonal tone?

Letter strings and pronunciation

1 Complete the answers to the clues in the table below. The answers are all words which contain the **ch** letter string. The first letter of each word has been given.

Clue	Answer
A place where children go to learn.	S
A bird which lays eggs commonly eaten.	C
I am made of bread.	S
I am a group of musicians.	O
I have one on my wrist which tells the time.	W
People who live in Holland.	D
Often put on chips.	K

2 Say each word in the bubble and listen to the pronunciation of the **ch** letter string.
Sort the words into two columns to show the different pronunciations of this letter string.

research   mischief   Christmas
exchange   technical   choir
stomach   chase

Sounds like *ch*	Sounds like *c*

3 Circle the words below that have a **soft c** sound (the **s phoneme**)
Use each word in a sentence of your own.

catalogue
celebration
dance cancel
princess recipe
certificate column
catastrophe
character

_____

_____

_____

_____

_____

4 Complete the words in these sentences with **ant, ent, ance, ence**.

a The pres_____ of the adult meant that the behaviour of the children was excell_____.

b The old man was hesit_____ as he approached his front door.

c The appear_____ of the famous pop star at the perform_____ was greeted with loud cheers.

d Mary was reluct_____ to get up.

e The ch_____ of doing a sci_____ experiment was viewed as exciting by the children.

f The resid_____ had lived in the street a long time.

The conditional sentence

1 Complete the following sentences using a conditional clause.

a I can help _____ .

b You should have asked the teacher _____ .

c We might go _____ .

d I wouldn't do that _____ .

e You ought to take your raincoat _____ .

f She will be late for school _____ .

2 Write three sentences with the word 'unless'. This means 'if not'. For example, *'Unless you behave you will be asked to leave the room.'*

_____

_____

_____

3 Write three sentences with the word 'provided'. This means 'only if'. For example, *'Provided you bring along some money, you are welcome to attend the show.'*

_____

_____

_____

4 Write three sentences with the phrase 'As long as' to say something will happen only on the condition something else happens. For example, *'As long as you are here on time, you can come along.'*

_____

_____

_____

Features of written arguments

Read through this one-sided argument on whether children should be allowed to bring mobile phones to school, and then answer the questions on page 30.

Should children be allowed to bring mobile phones to school?

Some children feel they should be able to bring their mobile phones to school. However, if this were to happen, this could create significant problems – all of which could seriously affect the quality of teaching and learning.

Firstly, if children were allowed to have mobile phones in the classroom, this could disrupt lessons. Although children might say that their phone is switched off, this might not always be the case – and teachers do not have enough time to carry out regular checks.

In addition, children would be constantly checking their bags to see if they had a message or a missed call. How is the teacher – busy enough as it is – meant to keep an eye on this? Indeed, on those occasions when the teacher is working with a group of children, some children would see this as an opportunity to play games on their smartphone, rather than concentrating on their work. Teachers should be teaching, not supervising phone use.

Some children have suggested that teachers could take their phones in when they first come to school in the morning. But what then would be the point of bringing the phones to school? And do we really want a teacher's time to be spent counting in phones at the beginning and end of the day? What happens if they get mixed up?

Research shows that children see their mobile phone as a central part of their life, and so find it difficult to ignore calls and text messages. In another recent study, it was shown that children's concentration dipped significantly when they had a mobile phone in their possession.

Of course, children may need to contact parents (and vice versa), but the school has a telephone that children are allowed to use at break, lunchtime and after school. Equally, the school office is happy to take phone calls from parents, and pass that message on to the child.

Children come to school to work, to learn, to achieve. They need to learn in an environment which is free from distraction, and one in which they can fully concentrate. Both parents and children need to accept that mobile phones and school do not, and should not, mix.

Features of written arguments

2 List two main arguments the writer makes against bringing mobile phones to school.

_____

_____

3 Read the argument on page 29 again. Each paragraph puts forward a main argument, and then supports it with examples. Highlight the main argument in each paragraph in one colour, and the supporting information in another.

4 Give three connectives used in the argument to order and link the points being made.

_____

_____

_____

5 Find one example of each of the following.

Language feature	Example
A set of three	
Rhetorical question	
Short sentence for effect	
Adverb used for emphasis	
Exaggerated opinion	
Use of conditional to present an argument	
Confident phrase	

6 On a separate piece of paper, write down three phrases or sentences you thought were effective in making the argument.

A balanced argument

 Read through this example of a balanced argument on whether cars should be banned from the centre of towns and cities.

Has the time come to ban cars from the centre of towns and cities?

Global warming caused by pollution has begun to affect us, with climate change starting to affect British weather. Some people believe the time has come for drastic action to reduce pollution caused by heavy traffic.

There is no doubt that traffic fumes are a major cause of pollution throughout the developed world, and cause problems in large towns and cities. In a small country like the UK, cities are close enough together to cause high levels of traffic fumes. Consequently, health problems are created such as asthma. Indeed, this has rapidly increased as the number of cars on the road has risen. An additional problem in urban areas is traffic congestion, which wastes time and adds to costs. The average speed of traffic in central London is now only 12 miles an hour – the same as it was in Victorian times. A ban on cars in the centre of large towns and cities would therefore seem sensible as it would cut pollution, thereby improving health. It would also reduce traffic congestion, allowing buses, emergency vehicles and delivery trucks to get to their destination.

On the other hand, it could be argued that such a ban would create other problems. Public transport in the UK is expensive and sometimes unreliable. Would there be enough trains and buses to cope with the numbers needing them? Furthermore, there is also the issue of personal freedom. Is it right to prevent people from choosing the mode of transport they prefer? Many people feel safer in their cars when travelling at night than they do on a bus or a train.

While there is clearly an urgent need to cut pollution, this could be achieved by developing cleaner fuels and electrically powered cars, and encouraging people to use public transport where possible, rather than forcing them to do so. Perhaps we are not ready to ban cars from the centre of our towns and cities.

A balanced argument

2 Read the argument on page 31 again.
  a Give two of the main arguments against cars/transport.
  b Give two of the main arguments for keeping cars/transport.
  c Identify the phrase which introduces the counterargument:
    On the other hand.

3 Write down two facts and two opinions used in the article.

Fact	Opinion

4 Use the planning frame below to plan ideas for a balanced argument about whether children should decide on the time they go to bed, and not parents. Ideas for the first paragraph have been written for you. Then write your balanced argument on page 33.

> **Paragraph 1**
>
> The argument of whether children should decide what time they go to bed or their parents is a complex one, with reasons both for and against.

Paragraph 2 Arguments for	**Paragraph 3** Arguments against

Connective phrases	Vocabulary

> **Paragraph 4** Conclusions

A balanced argument

5 Write your balanced argument here.

_____

_____

_____

_____

_____

_____

_____

_____

_____

_____

_____

_____

_____

_____

_____

_____

_____

_____

_____

_____

_____

_____

Now check your writing for accurate grammar, punctuation and spelling.

Self-assessment

Unit 3

Reports and argument

	I understand this well
	I understand this but need more practice
☹	I don't understand this

Learning Objectives	☺	😐	☹
Phonics, spelling and vocabulary			
I can point out all the word endings with different spellings but the same pronunciation.			
I can apply spelling patterns and be accurate in spelling.			
Grammar and punctuation			
I know how to use a conditional sentence in an argument.			
I know how to use active and passive verbs within a sentence.			
Reading: Non-fiction			
I can recognise the key features of a balanced argument text.			
I can tell the difference between fact and opinion.			
I can recognise the features of a non-chronological text.			
Writing: Non-fiction			
I can write a non-chronological report using paragraphs.			
I can write a balanced report.			
I can argue a case in writing, developing points logically and convincingly.			
Speaking and listening			
I can present an argument to an audience effectively.			

_____

_____

_____

_____

I need more help with ...

Non-fiction: reading and writing skills

Explicit and implicit questions

 Read this article about sharks.

Save our Sharks

Over the last year alone, I've had the great privilege of many hours underwater with sharks of various shapes and sizes. Every encounter has been a true wonder. I've also found out through experience quite how harmless to humans these ancient animals really are.

My favourite encounter by far was with blue sharks, a species common to British waters. While free diving alongside them in the open ocean, a group stayed with us for hours, and never more than few feet from our masks. One huge blue must have been 3.5 m long, but nuzzled up against me like a big friendly pet. If I had been more sentimental, I would have taken his gentle nosing to be affection!

Yet, this may be an experience the next generation will not be able to share. Between 2000 and 2012, more than half a million tonnes of blue shark was caught in the Atlantic – that is approximately 13 million sharks. In fact, 97% of sharks caught from the Atlantic are called 'no limit' species – so fishermen can bring in as many of them as they want. That's why I am supporting the Shark Trust's 'No Limits?' campaign.

The 'No Limits?' campaign needs everyone to support the limits for catching sharks by signing an on-line petition urging governments to act before it's too late and ensure Atlantic shark populations can continue to survive and thrive in our oceans.

2 Answer these explicit questions.

a Give evidence from the text that shows the writer has been swimming with sharks underwater. _____

b What size can sharks grow to? _____

c How many sharks have been caught by fishermen?_____

d What is the 'No Limits?' campaign? _____

e What does the writer want readers to do? _____

Explicit and implicit meaning

1 Read the article on page 35 again and answer these **implicit** questions.

a How does the reader know the blue shark is not the only species of shark the writer has swum with?

_____

b Give two pieces of evidence from the text which suggests sharks are not dangerous to humans.

_____

c The writer is obviously impressed by sharks. Find two words/phrases which show this.

_____

d What do you think the writer would like to say to shark fishermen?

_____

2 Find words in the passage which mean the same as:

a A special advantage given to a particular person. (p_____)
b Meet something. (e_____)
c From a long time ago. (a_____)
d To work in an organised way towards a goal. (c_____)
e Roughly, round about. (a_____)
f Trying hard to persuade someone to do something. (u_____)

3 On a separate piece of paper, use half a page to copy the table below. Draw an image in each of the boxes to show what each of the paragraphs on page 35 are about. For example, the first box might show a diver and lots of sharks.

Add a suitable quotation from each paragraph beneath each image.

Image for paragraph 1	Image for paragraph 2
Quotation from paragraph 1	Quotation from paragraph 2
Image for paragraph 3	Image for paragraph 4
Quotation from paragraph 3	Quotation from paragraph 4

Colons

 1 Add a colon to these sentences, followed by a list of appropriate items. Remember the rule for using colons is to separate the items in a list using commas.

a   There are many different varieties of sweets: _____

_____

_____

b   Everything they had was lost in the fire: _____

_____

c   I need to take these things on holiday: _____

_____

 2 A colon is also used to show that two sentences are connected – for example, through cause and effect. Match up these eight sentences below, making them into four sentences, each with a colon.

a   The weather forecast was wrong: she felt so ill.

b   Malaki rushed across the road: it rained all day.

c   The cake was delicious: the result was a terrible accident.

d   Junita could not speak: everyone ate it.

3 Write these sentences out using the colon correctly.

a   Emperor Kangxi was born in 1654 he died in: 1722.

_____

b   Here is what I would like: you to bring to the party a large cake, food and a new music video.

_____

_____

c   I really enjoyed: the speaker he was very interesting.

_____

d   Bring everything you need: for a holiday sun tan cream, swimming costume and a good book.

_____

_____

37

Semi-colons

A semi-colon can be used **instead of** a conjunction 'and' or 'but' to join the sentences as long as the first sentence is related to the second. Re-write each pair of sentences as one sentence. Use a semi-colon to link them. Remember to lose the capital letter in between the sentences.

a   The red team won. The blue team was exhausted.

_____

b   I went to bed late last night. This morning I got up early.

_____

c   He hated sports. She loved them.

_____

d   The door swung open. A large man strode in.

_____

e   Mariyah was given a new doll. She played with it for hours.

_____

f   Ishaq's birthday is in June. Gideon's birthday is in July.

_____

Add a list of items separated by a semi-colon to each of the following. Remember the three word rule!

a   To make a cake you need these ingredients:

_____

b   For the game of tennis, you will need to bring this equipment:

_____

c   The presents I still need to buy for my family are as follows:

_____

On a separate piece of paper, write sentences using a semi-colon/s:

a   A sentence in which you describe someone who has two sides to their personality.
b   A sentence in which you compare two friends who are very different.
c   A sentence in which you list your favourite foods.
d   A sentence in which you begin with high hopes of a country/place, then show disappointment.
e   A sentence in which you list the qualities you like about each of your friends.

Brackets and dashes

1 Brackets keep additional information from the rest of the sentence.
Add the correct additional information to each sentence below, using brackets.

> a parakeet   Jakarta   a football team
> author of *Matilda*   December 25th

a Manchester United _____ is famous all over the world.

b The capital of Indonesia _____ is full of traffic.

c Christmas Day _____ is a popular celebration in many parts of the world.

d Roald Dahl _____ is a famous children's writer.

e The Indian Ringneck _____ has a hooked beak.

2 Re-write the sentences above so that the information in brackets is separated by parenthetic commas, for example, *Anu Kumar, an author, came to visit our school.*

a _____

b _____

c _____

d _____

e _____

What difference did this make?

_____

3 A dash keeps words apart often for deliberate effect, so the reader notices the separated word/s. Add a dash to each of these sentences.

a I bought my sister a present a white mouse.

b My brother loves spinach I hate it.

c I saw a frightening film last night 'The Haunted House!'

d I bought a new house in the Bahamas!

e She waited for a letter to come but nothing came.

4 Add a dash to the end of each sentence below, and then some more information. Remember that the dash is used deliberately to emphasise a part of the sentence which is dramatic, unexpected or amusing.

a She opened the door _____

b Down the road came a runaway car _____

c He looked down _____

d The woman rushed across the street_____

Self-assessment

Unit 4

Non-fiction and writing skills

 I understand this well

 I understand this but need more practice

 I don't understand this

Learning Objectives			
Phonics, spelling and vocabulary			
I can suggest alternative words with the same shades of meaning.			
Grammar and punctuation			
I can identify the colon and use it correctly.			
I can identify the semi-colon and use it correctly.			
I can identify brackets and use them correctly.			
I can identify the use of the dash and use it correctly.			
I can point out the main clause and other clauses in a complex sentence.			
I can use punctuation effectively such as commas to mark out meaning in a sentence.			
Reading: Non-fiction			
I can look for implicit meanings, and make inferences based on more than one point in the text.			
I can answer questions on explicit meanings based on information at more than one point in the text.			
Writing: Non-fiction			
I can use paragraphs to sequence and link my ideas.			
Speaking and listening			
I can listen well during a discussion and ask and answer questions.			
I can introduce a new idea to a discussion.			

_____

_____

_____

_____

I need more help with ...

Fiction: characters and settings

Creating an interesting sentence

 To these sentences, add an adverb, an adjective and change the verb so that you have a much more interesting sentence.

a She ran along the road.

b The boy shouted across the classroom.

c The birds flew across the sky on their way to Africa.

d I like cake.

e He kicked the ball into the air.

 Many common words can be used as adverbs:

> almost, never, far, always, well, often, really, sometimes, seldom, again

Choose five of these adverbs and write a sentence using each of them. Remember, an adverb gives more information about a verb.

_____

_____

_____

_____

_____

3 Write a paragraph describing the main street in your town or village, or near where you live. Use adjectives, adverbs and verbs to bring the scene to life.

_____

_____

_____

_____

_____

_____

Settings and characters

 Read the following setting and character descriptions.

Setting

i   The cottage was small, square and comfortable: coming to live here had been like putting on an old coat. It had a sagging slate roof; a bulge at one end where there had been a bread oven; huge beams, creaking stairs and stone floor, with interesting cracks from which emerged at night, large and stately black beetles.

---

ii It was dark-winter dusk. Snow lay white and shining over the pleated hills, and frost hung from the forest trees. Snow lay piled on the dark road across Willoughby World, but from dawn men had been clearing it with brooms and shovels. There were hundreds of them at work, wrapped in sacking because of the bitter cold, and keeping together in groups for fear of the wolves, savage and reckless from hunger.

Character

iii At that moment there was a commotion from downstairs, and Bonnie turned, her face alight with expectancy. She flew recklessly along the huge expanse of nursery floor, gleaming and polished as glass, and down the main staircase to the entrance hall. Her impetuosity brought her to the feet of an immensely tall, thin lady, clad from neck to toe in a travelling dress of swathed grey twill, with a stiff collar, dark glasses and dull, green buttoned boots.

---

iv James had noticed him vaguely at school, a short stumpy boy, with immensely thick, round glasses. He set off for Simon's house, which was at the end of the lane, towards the High Street. Simon was conveniently available outside his house, lying along the top of a stone wall. His **bespectacled** face stared down at James like an amiable **gargoyle**. 'Hello', he said in a friendly, unconcerned voice, not at all like someone who was responsible for some kind of trick.

Word bank

bespectacled: wearing spectacles
gargoyle: a distorted carving of a human or animal face

a   In extract (i) underline and label six adjectives, one example of alliteration, one example of a simile.

b   In extract (ii) underline and label six adjectives, three verbs.

c   In extract (iii) underline and label six adjectives, three verbs, one adverb, one simile.

d   In extract (iv) underline and label six adjectives, two adverbs, one simile.

Use the following codes for the labels:
A   = adjective
Al = alliteration
S   = simile
V   = verb
Ad = adverb

Setting descriptions

 1 Read this extract from *Swami and Friends* by R. K. Narayan. Swaminathan and his friend Mani are sitting by a river in the early evening.

River Sarayu was the pride of Malgudi. It was some ten minutes' walk from Ellaman Street, the last street of the town, chiefly occupied by **oil mongers**. Its sandbanks were the evening resort of all the people of the town. The Municipal President took any distinguished visitor to the top of the town hall and proudly pointed out to him Sarayu in moonlight, glistening like a silver belt across the north.

The usual evening crowd was on the sand. Swaminathan and Mani sat aloof on a river-step, with their legs dangling in the water. The **peepul** branches overhanging the river rustled pleasantly. A light breeze played about the **boughs** and scattered stray leaves on the gliding stream below. Birds filled the air with their cries. Far away, near Nallappa's Mango Grove, a little downstream, a herd of cattle was crossing the river. And then a country cart drawn by bullocks passed, the cart-man humming a low tune. It was some fifteen minutes past sunset and there was a soft red in the west.

Word bank

oil monger: a person who sells oil
peepul: a type of tree
bough: a branch of a tree

a List two features which make this description effective.

_____

b List three verbs you find effective.

_____

c List three adjectives you find effective.

_____

Writing a story

Read this extract from *Stig of the Dump* by Clive King. A young boy is out exploring and has spotted the bottom of a pit. A pit is a large hole in the ground.

He crawled through the rough grass and peered over. The sides of the pit were white chalk, with lines of flint poking out like bones in places. At the top was crumbly brown earth and the roots of trees that grew on the edge. The roots looped over the edge, twined in the air and grew back into the earth. Some of the trees hung over the edge, holding on desperately by a few roots. The earth and chalk had fallen beneath them, and one day they too would fall to the bottom of the pit.

Far below was the bottom of the pit. The dump. Barney could see strange bits of wreckage among the moss and elder bushes and nettles. Was that the steering wheel of a ship? The tail of an aeroplane?
At least there was a real bicycle. Barney felt sure he could make it go if only he could get at it. They did not let him have a bicycle.

Barney wished he was at the bottom of the pit.

And the ground gave away.

Write what happens next. You will need to try and write in the same style as the writer. Finish the writing at an exciting point. You are only expected to write two or three paragraphs. You may want to add your own illustration and continue on more paper if necessary.

Check your writing for grammar, punctuation and spelling.

Word classes

1 Find the following adjectives which could be used instead of 'old' and 'young' in this word search.

```
v  e  l  p  n  o  s  i  o  n  b  q
s  a  g  e  d  t  o  s  i  m  y  l
d  n  i  m  m  a  t  u  r  e  o  h
b  c  v  o  f  s  l  p  j  c  u  u
d  i  n  l  r  i  w  e  r  h  t  l
r  e  l  d  e  r  l  y  u  i  h  p
f  n  g  e  s  h  u  j  o  l  f  c
e  t  x  r  h  b  z  n  m  d  u  w
m  s  d  j  j  u  v  e  n  i  l  e
e  b  t  e  r  w  u  m  i  s  o  j
m  a  t  u  r  e  p  l  a  h  q  u
n  x  r  b  e  t  t  y  i  l  n  g
```

Old:
ancient
aged
older
mature
elderly
Young:
youthful
immature
childish
juvenile
fresh

2 Insert the verbs that are missing in the right place.

scanning	picked	raises	sprouts	stands

Early morning grows into mid-morning, and mid-morning _____ wings and becomes a hot, sun-blasted afternoon. Unless there's a customer _____ the shelves, Danny _____ at the door, cold bottle of Coke in his hand, watching the cars pass on Main Street and the people walk by. Everyone seeming like they have things to do and places to go. By around three, business has _____ up, same as it always does, and that keeps him busy and away from the sunshine, until finally he _____ his head and it's coming up to seven in the evening and his favourite time of the week.

Adapted from Skulduggery Pleasant, The Dying of the Light by Derek Landy

3 Complete these phrases using the most appropriate adverb.

noisily	angrily	loudly	excitedly	softly

a whispered _____   b cheered _____
c snarled _____   d snored _____
e shouted _____

4 On a separate piece of paper, re-write these sentences, replacing the words in italics with adverbs.

a The windows were closed *in a hurry.*
b The cat was lying *in peace* in the afternoon sun.
c He played the piano *with skill* and *care.*
d Our grandmother comes to visit us *now and again.*
e The driver drove the car *with caution.*
f *At last* the special day arrived.

Settings and shades of meaning

1 Underline a word in each line that has a similar meaning to the word on the left in bold.

tranquil	comfort	calm	tense	obedient
agitated	misfortune	onslaught	hopeful	restless
moist	mysterious	soaking	muggy	damp
linger	loiter	inhabit	delay	lodge
hideous	spiteful	cold	repugnant	unfriendly
peak	heap	area	highest	bundle
accurate	truthful	precise	straightforward	frank

2 a In the space below, draw a picture of where you live – your home, the road and the environment around it, for example, the countryside.

b Fill each part of the drawing with words (adjectives, verbs, adverbs, nouns) that describe how you feel about it. For example, the road part of the drawing may have words such as: traffic, dusty, noisy, shouting.

c Use these words to help you write a short description of where you live on a separate piece of paper. Start your description like this: *Let me describe where I live ...*

Self-assessment

Unit 5

Characters and settings

	I understand this well
	I understand this but need more practice
	I don't understand this

Learning Objectives	☺	😐	☹
Phonics, spelling and vocabulary			
I can use words with different shades of meaning.			
I can use new words in context in my work.			
Grammar and punctuation			
I know about different word classes such as the noun, verb, adjective and adverb.			
I can talk about the grammatical features of fiction texts.			
I can use punctuation effectively when writing to mark out meaning in complex sentences.			
Reading: Fiction			
I can talk about how characters and settings are presented by the author.			
I can give reasons why or why not I like a text.			
I can comment on the writer's use of language and how it effects the reader.			
Writing: Fiction			
I can plan a story with a plot, characters and setting.			
I can use paragraphs, sequencing and linking them appropriately.			
I can develop some imaginative detail through careful use of vocabulary.			
Speaking and listening			
I can take on a role confidently.			
I can speak my views clearly in a discussion.			

I need more help with ...

_____

_____

_____

Techniques for reading and writing fiction

Fiction genres

1   Here are some different fiction genres. Give three key features of each.

Real life adventure	
Science fiction	
Fairy tale	
Myth	

2   Can you find these fiction genres in the word search?

```
e  e  b  n  s  h  o  o  p  s  h
c  r  v  z  j  l  f  e  e  p  s
n  q  w  u  i  l  o  m  n  g  t
a  x  e  r  i  a  e  l  p  y  y
m  e  s  t  e  n  a  r  g  a  r
o  r  t  g  a  n  g  s  t  e  r
r  e  e  p  u  r  c  r  i  m  e
h  o  r  r  o  r  e  v  e  l  e
u  n  n  p  e  l  d  o  l  p  f
y  n  s  c  h  o  o  l  e  n  g
```

horror
crime
romance
western
school
gangster

3   What is your favourite genre? Give three reasons why.

_____

_____

_____

_____

_____

_____

_____

Story beginnings

1 What type of story beginning are each of the following an example of? Choose from:

time of day   dialogue   setting   character   flashback

a I remember it as if it was yesterday.	
b 'Can I come with you?' she asked, pleadingly.	
c From a distance, the houses appeared small and lost, heavily shrouded in the grey November mist.	
d It was a warm summer evening, and still warm enough to sit outside in the garden.	
e Malakai Bennett, his face screwed up in anger, kicked the large stone as hard as he could.	

2 Draw an illustration for one of the beginnings.

3 Choose another beginning and write a bullet point list of what you think could happen next.

Ideas

Dialogue

 Underline the words that are not direct speech.

> 'Yes, yes!' cried Barney, 'It's just down by the lane. Come on!' And he took the policeman by the hand and pulled him through the iron gate, and down the lane, explaining as he went.
>
> He led the way to the top of the cliff where the car had gone over and pointed, 'It's down there,' he said.
>
> The policeman looked over, 'I can't see anything,' he said.

2 Here is more of the conversation between Barney and the policeman. Write it out again, adding comment so that the reader is able to see the character – their movement, facial expressions and how they speak and say the words.

> 'Of course not, we buried it. Come on down and see.' (Barney)
>
> 'Look, son. There's been three houses burgled in this district, and it's my job to get the valuables back. And I haven't got a lot of time to waste.' (policeman)
>
> 'It's down here. I'll show it to you if you just come down.' (Barney)

_____

_____

_____

_____

_____

_____

3 Imagine you and a friend discover something unusual in the field or woods near where you live. Write the conversation which takes place. Remember to build in details which will enable the reader to see the characters – their movement, facial expression and how they speak and say the words. The conversation could start like this:

'Hey, what's that over there? There's something in the grass …,' George whispered quietly, his face white with apprehension.

Using a paragraph plan

1 Write down what you have learned about writing an effective story. For example:
- paragraph plan
- particular type of beginning: flashback, dialogue, description.

_____

_____

_____

_____

_____

_____

2 Here is a paragraph plan for a story. Draw what is happening in each paragraph.

Paragraph 1	Boy wakes up. Realises he is late for school.	
Paragraph 2	No time to get dressed properly, or have any breakfast.	
Paragraph 3	Runs for school bus, but he trips, hurting his leg.	
Paragraph 4	Boy back in bed with a bandaged leg – eating his breakfast.	

Writing a story using a paragraph plan

1 Write the story using the paragraph plan from page 51. You could use these paragraph beginnings. Remember to show, and not tell. If you decide to use any dialogue, add in details of character movement, facial expression and how they speak.

Paragraph 1: Oh no, it was 8.30 a.m.

_____

_____

_____

_____

_____

Paragraph 2: Dashing down stairs …

_____

_____

_____

_____

_____

Paragraph 3: The bus was just moving off, so …

_____

_____

_____

_____

_____

Paragraph 4: One hour later …

_____

_____

_____

_____

_____

_____

Remember to check your writing for accurate spelling, grammar and punctuation.

Self-assessment

Unit 6

Techniques for reading and writing fiction

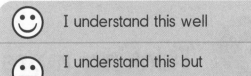

	☺ I understand this well
	☺ I understand this but need more practice
	☹ I don't understand this

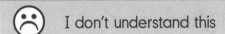

Learning Objectives	☺	😐	☹
Phonics, spelling and vocabulary			
I know how to apply spelling patterns and be accurate in my spelling.			
Grammar and punctuation			
I can use speech marks correctly.			
I can use a range of punctuation to make my writing interesting.			
Reading: Fiction			
I can point out implicit meanings in a text.			
I know how the structure of narrative works.			
I understand how characters and settings are presented by an author.			
Writing: Fiction			
I know the features of different fiction genres.			
I can plan a plot with characters and structure it effectively.			
I can use paragraphs, sequencing and linking them appropriately to support overall development of my writing.			
I can develop some imaginative detail through careful use of vocabulary.			
Speaking and listening			
I can vary the expression and tone of my voice when reading aloud.			
I can prepare, practise and improve a spoken performance.			

I need more help with ...

_____

_____

_____

_____

Thinking more about poetry

'The Highwayman'

 Read this beginning extract from the poem, 'The Highwayman' by Alfred Noyes, and then answer the questions which follow. In the time before there were any cars, a highwayman was a man on horseback who robbed travellers.

The wind was a torrent of darkness among the gusty trees.
The moon was a ghostly galleon* tossed upon cloudy seas.
The road was a ribbon of moonlight over the purple moor,
And the highwayman came riding—
Riding—riding—
The highwayman came riding, up to the old inn-door.

He'd a French cocked-hat on his forehead, a bunch of lace at his chin,
A coat of the claret* velvet, and breeches of brown doe-skin.
They fitted with never a wrinkle: his boots were up to the thigh!
And he rode with a jewelled twinkle,
His pistol butts a-twinkle,
His rapier* hilt a-twinkle, under the jewelled sky.

'The Highwayman' *by Alfred Noyes*

2 Answer these questions.

a Write down the meanings of the words with a * next to them. You will need to use a dictionary.

galleon   _____

claret   _____

rapier   _____

b What is the rhyming scheme used in the poem? Remember to write it down like this: aa, bb, etc.

_____

c Give an example of alliteration from the poem.

_____

d List the three colours mentioned in the poem.

_____

e Explain **why** it seemed as if the highwaymen 'rode with a jewelled twinkle'.

_____

More about 'The Highwayman'

 Read this next part of 'The Highwayman'. The highwayman has arranged to meet the landlord's daughter. The man who looks after the horses (an ostler) watches them. He is jealous as he also loves the landlord's daughter. The highwayman tells the landlord's daughter that he will be back again to take her away with him.

Over the cobbles he clattered and clashed in the dark inn-yard.
And he tapped with his whip on the shutters, but all was locked and barred.
He whistled a tune to the window, and who should be waiting there
But the landlord's black-eyed daughter,
Bess, the landlord's daughter,
Plaiting a dark red love-knot into her long black hair.

And dark in the dark old inn-yard a stable-wicket creaked
Where Tim the ostler listened; his face was white and peaked.
His eyes were hollows of madness, his hair like mouldy hay,
But he loved the landlord's daughter,
The landlord's red-lipped daughter.
Dumb as a dog he listened, and he heard the robber say—

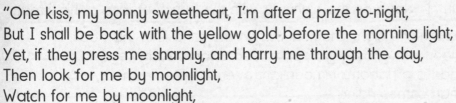

"One kiss, my bonny sweetheart, I'm after a prize to-night,
But I shall be back with the yellow gold before the morning light;
Yet, if they press me sharply, and harry me through the day,
Then look for me by moonlight,
Watch for me by moonlight,
I'll come to thee by moonlight, though hell should bar the way."

2 Give one example of each of the following from the poem

Feature	Example
repetition	
onomatopoeia	
simile	
alliteration	

3 What is your favourite line in the poem? Write it down here. Can you explain why you like it?

_____

_____

_____

_____

The ending of 'The Highwayman'

Here is the ending of 'The Highwayman'. The jealous ostler, Tim, has told the soldiers (known as red-coats) about the highwayman coming back to the inn, so they are waiting for him. However, the landlord's daughter hears him coming, and warns him by turning the gun on herself. The gun (a musket) would have made a loud noise.

He turned; he spurred to the west; he did not know who stood
Bowed, with her head o'er the musket, drenched with her own red blood!
Not till the dawn he heard it, his face grew grey to hear
How Bess, the landlord's daughter,
The landlord's black-eyed daughter,
Had watched for her love in the moonlight, and died in the darkness there.

Back, he spurred like a madman, shrieking a curse to the sky,
With the white road smoking behind him and his rapier brandished high.
Blood-red were his spurs in the golden noon; wine-red was his velvet coat;
When they shot him down on the highway,
Down like a dog on the highway,
And he lay in his blood on the highway, with the bunch of lace at his throat.

And still of a winter's night, they say, when the wind is in the trees,
When the moon is a ghostly galleon tossed upon cloudy seas,
When the road is a ribbon of moonlight over the purple moor,
A highwayman comes riding—
Riding—riding—
A highwayman comes riding, up to the old inn-door.

Over the cobbles he clatters and clangs in the dark inn-yard.
He taps with his whip on the shutters, but all is locked and barred.
He whistles a tune to the window, and who should be waiting there
But the landlord's black-eyed daughter,
Bess, the landlord's daughter,
Plaiting a dark red love-knot into her long black hair.

'The Highwayman'

Read the poem on page 56 and answer these questions.

a Make up five questions for a partner to answer on this last part of the poem. Here are some areas you could focus on:

alliteration	repetition	onomatopoeia
simile	implicit question	explicit question
metaphor	colours	verbs	adjectives

b Write your questions here. Leave room for your partner to answer.

Question 1
Question 2
Question 3
Question 4
Question 5

You have studied 5 poems:

'Silver' by Walter De La Mare (Learner's Book page 98)

'The Listeners' by Walter De La Mare (Learner's Book pages 104–105)

'Wind' by Christina Rossetti (Learner's Book page 102)

'The Whistling Wind' by Wang Xiaoni (Learner's Book page 102)

'The Highwayman' by Alfred Noyes

Which one did you like the best and why? Write your answer on a separate piece of paper. Remember to give three or four reasons for your preference.

Words borrowed from other countries

1 Using a prefix or suffix, make two words out of each of the following roots.

port (carry)	
jec or ject (throw)	
pos, pon or pose (to place or put)	
struct (to build)	
multi (many)	
therm (heat)	
logy (study of)	

2 **a** The English names for the days of the week come from the Anglo-Saxons. These were two German tribes who invaded England in the 5th century. Many words in English are derived from the Anglo-Saxon.

Match the days of the week with its Anglo-Saxon origin.

Sunnandaeg	Wednesday
Saeternesdaeg	Thursday
Monandaeg	Friday
Wodnesdaeg	Saturday
Tiwesdaeg	Monday
Thunresdaeg	Sunday
Frigesdaeg	Tuesday

b The English names for the months of the year come from the Romans. They invaded Great Britain over **2000** years ago.

Write in the name of the month next to the Roman origin word.

Junius	
Aprilis	
Augustus	
Maritus	
Februarius	
Maius	

3 Complete these sentences using these words.

spaghetti	bungalow	pyjamas	cul-de-sac
au revoir	jungle	shampoo	chow mein

At the end of the sentence, write which country (France, India, China, Italy) the word originated from.

a We like _____ with tomato sauce. _____

b A _____ is a house with no upstairs. _____

c _____ are clothes worn in bed. _____

d I wash my hair with _____. _____

e _____ is another way of saying goodbye. _____

f A _____ is a street with a dead end. _____

g _____ is a dish of meat, vegetables and fried noodles. _____

h Lions live in the _____. _____

Exploring feelings through poetry

1 Poems can make the reader think about many different feelings. One feeling is one of laughter and delight. Read this poem by Alfred Noyes.

The Day Daddy Fell Into the Pond

Everyone grumbled. The sky was grey.
We had nothing to do and nothing to say.
We were nearing the end of a dismal day,
And then there seemed to be nothing beyond,
Then
Daddy fell into the pond!

And everyone's face grew merry and bright,
And Timothy danced for sheer delight.
"Give me the camera, quick, oh quick!
He's crawling out of the duckweed!" Click!

Then the gardener suddenly slapped his knee,
And doubled up, shaking silently,
And the ducks all quacked as if they were daft,
And it sounded as if the old drake laughed.
Oh, there wasn't a thing that didn't respond
When
Daddy fell into the pond!

The Day Daddy Fell Into the Pond by Alfred Noyes

2 Someone has fallen into a pond. Give three ways the poet has made this seem amusing to the reader.

_____

_____

_____

3 Look at how the first part of the poem is presented and laid out below:

Everyone grumbled. The sky was grey.
We had nothing to do and nothing to say.
We were nearing the end of a dismal day.
And there seemed to be nothing beyond,

THEN
Daddy
    fell
       into
          the
             pond!

Re-write another verse of the poem, presenting it so as to make it more amusing and interesting for the reader. You may want to add an illustration.

Self-assessment

Unit 7

Thinking more about poetry

😊	I understand this well	
😐	I understand this but need more practice	
😞	I don't understand this	

Learning Objectives	😊	😐	😞
Phonics, spelling and vocabulary			
I know how to transform the meaning of a word with prefixes and suffixes.			
I know about word origins and the use of words from other languages.			
I know about how words change over time.			
Grammar and punctuation			
I can point out different word classes in a text such as pronouns.			
Reading: Fiction and poetry			
I can explain how poets play with words and sounds in a text.			
I can read and understand poems in which meanings are implied.			
I can comment on a writer's use of language and how it effects the reaction of the reader.			
I can express what I like about a poem in terms of language, style and themes.			
I can explain how writing can evoke a particular mood.			
I can point out features which are the same in different poems.			
Writing: Fiction and poetry			
I can maintain a clear viewpoint when I am writing about my personal opinion.			
Speaking and listening			
I can become a character through my speech, gestures and movement.			
I can express my ideas clearly.			

_____

_____

_____   I need more help with ...

_____

Looking at Language

Adverbs, adjectives and prepositions

 1 Write a sentence using each of the following adverbs:

| really   very   regularly   now   so   yesterday |

_____

_____

_____

_____

_____

_____

2 Write five sentences which use the following adverbs: **frequently, occasionally, soon, somewhere, tomorrow** and include at least one adjective in each. Think about placing the adverb at different points in the sentence.

Sentence 1 _____

Sentence 2 _____

Sentence 3 _____

Sentence 4 _____

Sentence 5 _____

 3 a Fill in the missing letters in these prepositions.

fr__m

ac___ ___ss

b__tw___ ___n

thro___ ___gh

d___ ___n

w___ ___h

___p___n

b Match the pairs of prepositions with opposite meanings.

on	under
after	off
with	below
above	outside
over	before
inside	without

4 The agent is the 'doer' in a sentence. Sometimes, who took the action is not important. To get rid of the agent, write in the passive and drop the agent from the end of the sentence. Re-write these sentences into the passive, and remove the agent.

a The woman opened the door to the room.

b The man emptied the room of all its contents.

c The queen had left the jewellery box on the table.

d The child opened the box but it was empty.

The Little House on the Prairie

1 Read this extract from 'The Little House on the Prairie' by Laura Ingalls Wilder.

The family has found somewhere to live, but they do not have a source of fresh water. Pa decides to dig a well. A well is deep hole or shaft sunk into the earth to obtain water.

Next morning he marked a large circle in the grass near the corner of the house. With his spade he cut the **sod** inside the circle, and lifted it up in large pieces. The he began to shovel out the earth, digging himself deeper and deeper down.

Mary and Laura must not go near the well while Pa was digging. Even when they couldn't see his head anymore, shovelfuls of earth came flying up. At last the spade flew up and fell in the grass. Then Pa jumped. His hands caught hold of the sod, then one elbow gripped it, and then the other elbow, and with a heave Pa came rolling out. 'I can't throw the dirt out from any deeper,' he said.

He had to have help now. So he took his gun and rode away on Patty. When he came back he brought a plump rabbit, and he had traded work with Mr Scott. Mr Scott would help him dig this well, and then he would help dig Mr Scott's well.

Ma and Laura and Mary had not seen Mr and Mrs Scott. Their house was hidden somewhere in a little valley on the prairie. Laura had seen the smoke rising from it, and that was all. At dawn next morning, Mr Scott came. He was short and stout. His hair was bleached by the sun and his skin was bright red and scaly. He did not tan: he peeled.

'It's this blasted sun and wind,' he said. 'Beg your pardon, ma'am, but I might as well be a snake, the way I keep shedding my skin in this country.'

Laura liked him. Every morning, as soon as the dishes were washed and the beds were made, she ran out to watch Pa and Mr Scott working at the well. Mary preferred to stay in the house and sew on her patchwork quilt. But Laura liked the fierce light and the sun and the wind, and she couldn't stay away from the well. But she was not allowed to go near its edge...

> **Word bank**
> sod: grass and the part of the soil beneath it held together by the roots

2 Answer these questions.

a Explain the meaning of the sentence: '*I can't throw the dirt out from any deeper,*' he said. _____

b Explain the meaning of the sentence: *he had traded work with Mr Scott.*

_____

c We learn more about the characters in the text. Give evidence from the text which shows the following:

Character	Characteristic	Evidence from text
Pa	determined	
Mr Scott	polite	
Laura	bold	
Mary	reserved	

d List three adjectives used to describe Mr Scott.

_____

e Tick which theme applies to the extract.
perseverance ☐   hope ☐   love ☐   trust ☐   happiness ☐

Standard English

1 Re-write each sentence in Standard English.

a Who's got me book?

_____

b That's real nice of you.

_____

c I could of done it easy.

_____

d I haven't won no prizes.

_____

e We was just leaving.

_____

f I wishes I could go to Dubai on holiday.

_____

g We was late for school.

_____

2 Match up each saying with its correct meaning

To face the music   To overdo work and play

To hold one's tongue   To be exactly right

To burn the candle at both ends   To take punishment without complaint

To hang your head   To keep silent

To hit the nail on the head   To be ashamed of yourself

3 What do these common proverbs mean?

a Make hay while the sun shines.

_____

b Every cloud has a silver lining.

_____

c Out of the frying pan into the fire.

_____

Advertisements

Choose **one** of the following ideas to create an advertisement on a separate piece of paper.

Persuading readers to donate money to a local education book fund. The money from this will be used to buy more books for schools and raise children's literacy levels.

Persuading readers to buy a new drink or sandwich suitable for a lunchtime snack. The selling point would be that it is not only tasty or delicious and liked by children, but also healthy with vitamins and nutrients, so would be approved of by parents.

Whatever advertisement you choose to do, ensure that most of the following features are included:

- personal pronouns
- a contraction
- a sentence beginning with 'and' or 'but'
- a dash
- a rhetorical question
- a set of opposites
- careful choice of nouns, verbs and adjectives.

Including these features will help make your advert persuasive, so that a reader would want to contribute to your appeal for school funds or to buy the sandwich/drink.

You may decide to only have two or three paragraphs. Remember, a paragraph must be about one particular topic even if it is only one line long!

Remember to ensure that each paragraph has a focus.

Self-assessment

Unit 8

Looking at language

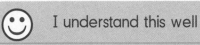
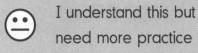 I understand this well

I understand this but
need more practice

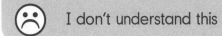 I don't understand this

Learning Objectives	🙂	😐	☹
Phonics, spelling and vocabulary			
I can spell words with different spellings but the same pronunciation.			
I can spot proverbs, sayings and figurative expressions in a text.			
Grammar and punctuation			
I can explain the language features of different types of text.			
I can point out standard and informal English in a text.			
I can point out different word classes: adjectives, adverbs and prepositions.			
I know how to use the active and passive voice.			
Reading: Non-fiction and fiction			
I can answer questions on implicit meaning.			
I can answer questions on the writer's use of language style and themes.			
I know about the key characteristics of an advertisement.			
I can point out fact and opinion in a text.			
Writing: Non-fiction			
I can use the features of an advertisement in my own writing.			
Speaking and listening			
I can speak confidently in a group situation.			
I can comment on variations in speech, and appropriate use of standard English.			

I need more help with ...

_____

_____

_____

_____

Unit 9 ## Suspense

Creating suspense

 Read this extract from the story, *Atisa and the Time Machine: In search of Kalidasa* by Anu Kumar.

Atisa leant forward, his heart beating fast. He knew for sure his sound catcher had picked up something distinct. He could hear the wind race into the balloon's folds, as he bent and raised the volume of the sound catcher. There was again a bubble and a clatter, then a bit later a voice broke through, speaking excitedly. It was in a language he did not understand, and something about the voice, the way it broke and the deep intonations that marked every sentence, and his own intuition, told Atisa for sure that he was hearing a voice from the past.

He felt a familiar rush of excitement. The wind pulled back his hair and made the hair on his arm stand up. Barely had the voice faded when he felt the wind rush at him and his machine. The wind thundered, drumming inside the balloon's folds and he held on fast as his cabin turned over again and again several times. He heard the voice and the crackles again, while the wind continued to blow. His machine bounced, swayed, whirled past clouds and turned over, but he held on fast, watching his breath mingle with fog as the clouds struck him on the face, and he tasted the mist on his lips time and again...

2 Answer these questions about the extract.

a Highlight/underline the features which create suspense.

b What do you think the sound catcher is?

_____

c Copy the sentence from the extract that suggests Atisa has experienced something similar to this before.

_____

d What do you think is going to happen next?

_____

Practising spelling

1 Write the correct spellings for these misspelt words.

a iliterate   _____

b irrattional   _____

c iresponsssible   _____

d illegiblle   _____

e iregular   _____

2 Add the right prefix to these words and then use them to complete the sentences.

a logical

b decisive

c relevant

d polite

If you cannot make up your mind you are being _____.

It is _____ not to say thank you.

The way in which you have approached that problem is _____.

Whether you like rice or not is _____.

3 Tick the words which have antonyms in the box and cross out the words which do not.

careless	brighten	hot	line	fast	bold	glass
careful	rough	cold	timid	slow	fade	bottle

4 Change these nouns into adjectives.

a happiness   _____

b sadness   _____

c quietness   _____

d loudness   _____

e cheerfulness _____

f emptiness   _____

Use each one to write a sentence of your own.

a _____

b _____

c _____

d _____

e _____

f _____

Playscript and suspense

 Read this extract from a suspense story. Answer the questions.

It started last week when I first heard the sounds. At first, I felt sure I was going mad. But when things in my room began to move from place to place, I knew I wasn't losing my mind. Something was definitely happening and someone, or something, was making it happen. At first I suspected my brother, but the sounds did not seem to come from any earthly source. They were just whispers and groans from behind the furniture. And they stopped immediately when I bent down to listen to them …

a What things in the extract make the narrator feel uneasy?

_____

b Why does the narrator think he is going mad?

_____

c Who does the narrator suspect is making the sounds at first?

_____

d What or who do you think is making the sounds?

_____

 Imagine you were in the room and heard the sounds. Go on to tell a member of your family about it, or a friend. Write out the conversation like a playscript on a separate piece of paper. It could begin as shown below. When it is finished you could act this conversation out in front of the class with a partner.

Me: Mum, I just heard a strange noise coming from behind the chair in my bedroom …

Mum *(busy preparing dinner)*: Can you hand me that bag of rice? A strange sound? I hope it is not mice again.

Me: No, it's not mice. Mice don't move books and other things around. It doesn't sound like a mouse.

Self-assessment

Unit 9

Suspense

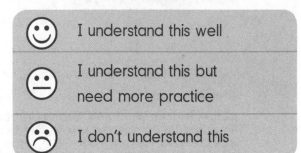

☺	I understand this well		
☺	I understand this but need more practice		
☹	I don't understand this		

Learning Objectives	☺	☺	☹
Phonics, spelling and vocabulary			
I can point out word roots, prefixes and suffixes, and know when to use double consonants.			
I know how to transform the meaning of a word with prefixes and suffixes.			
I know how to apply spelling patterns to improve accuracy in spelling.			
I can use words with shades of meaning and use new words.			
Grammar and punctuation			
I know about the language and grammatical features of different types of text.			
I can use speech marks and apostrophes correctly.			
Reading: Fiction			
I understand how an author creates suspense in a text.			
I can recognise implicit meanings in a text.			
I can point out what I like/dislike about a text.			
Writing: Fiction			
I can manage the development of an idea throughout a piece of writing.			
I can write a playscript effectively.			
Speaking and listening			
I can vary my vocabulary, expression and tone of voice to engage the listener.			
I can prepare, practise and improve a spoken presentation or performance.			
I can take on a character in role effectively.			

I need more help with ...

_____

_____

_____

_____

The Publishers would like to thank the following for permission to reproduce copyright material:

Acknowledgements

p2, from *The Grizzly Bear* by Abi Cushman, from http://www.animalfactguide.com/animal-facts/grizzly-bear; p2, from *Anne Frank, The Biography.com website*, 2014, (http://www.biography.com/people/anne-frank-9300892); p2, from *Why is the Ocean Blue?* by Lauren Orkus, 2014, http://www.whyzz.com/why-is-the-ocean-blue; p2, from *Huge Typhoon Hits Japan*, First News 11-17 July 2014; p3, from *NC boy credited with saving family from house fire,* July 6th 2014 (http://myfox8.com/2014/07/06/nc-boy-credited-with-saving-family-from-house-fire/); p7, from The Guardian, July 19th 2014; p13, from Charles Dickens at Wikipedia.org (2014) (http://en.wikipedia.org/wiki/Charles_Dickens) and reproduced under the Creative Commons Attribution-ShareAlike License (http://creativecommons.org/licenses/by-sa/3.0/); p16, from *Faster than Lightning: My Story* by Usain Bolt, reprinted by permission of HarperCollins Publishers Ltd. © 2013, Usain Bolt; p16, from *Jessica Ennis: Unbelievable* by Jessica Ennis published by Hodder and Stoughton, copyright © 2014 Jessica Ennis ; p21, from *The Wreck of the Zanzibar* by Michael Morpurgo , text copyright © 2012 Michael Morpurgo, published by Egmont UK Ltd; p22, from *The Ghost of Thomas Kempe* by Penelope Lively, text copyright © 1973 Penelope Lively, published by Egmont UK Ltd; p26, Text adapted from pages 14–15 of *The Changing Face of Nigeria* by Rob Bowden and Roy Maconachie, published by Hodder Wayland, 2004; p31, from *Has the time come to ban cars from the centre of towns and cities?* by Jim Usher (2008) from Primary Resources.co.uk (http://www.primaryresources.co.uk/english/docs/balanced_argument_examples.doc); p35, Adapted from Save our Sharks, First News (http://www.sharktrust.org/en/no_limits), 11-17 July 2014; p43, Extract from *Swami and Friends: A Malgudi Omnibus* by R.K. Narayan, published by Vintage Books; p44, p50 from *Stig of the Dump* by Clive King, published by Puffin Books Ltd; p45, Adapted from *The Dying of the Light, Skulduggery Pleasant* by Derek Landy, reprinted by permission of HarperCollins Publishers Ltd. © 2014, Derek Landy; p54, p55, p56, from *The Highwayman* by Alfred Noyes (1880-1958), used with permission of The Society of Authors as the Literary Representative of the Estate of Alfred Noyes; p59, from *The Day Daddy Fell in the Pond* by Alfred Noyes (1880-1958), used with permission of The Society of Authors as the Literary Representative of the Estate of Alfred Noyes; p62, from *Little House on The Prairie* by Laura Ingalls Wilder, published by HarperCollins; p66, Extract from *Atisa and the Time Machine: In Search of Kalidasa* by Anu Kumar published by Jaico Publishing House, Mumbai, *www.jaicobooks.com*; p68, Extract from p47 of *Caribbean Comprehension: an integrated, skills based approach, Book 5*, published by Hodder Education.

Every effort has been made to trace all copyright holders, but if any have been inadvertently overlooked the Publishers will be pleased to make the necessary arrangements at the first opportunity.

Although every effort has been made to ensure that website addresses are correct at time of going to press, Hodder Education cannot be held responsible for the content of any website mentioned in this book. It is sometimes possible to find a relocated web page by typing in the address of the home page for a website in the URL window of your browser.

Hachette Livre UK's policy is to use papers that are natural, renewable and recyclable products and made from wood grown in sustainable forests. The logging and manufacturing processes are expected to conform to the environmental regulations of the country of origin.

Orders: please contact Bookpoint Ltd, 130 Milton Park, Abingdon, Oxon OX14 4SB.
Telephone: +44 (0)1235 827720. Fax: +44 (0)1235 400454. Lines are open 9.00 a.m.–5.00 p.m., Monday to Saturday, with a 24-hour message answering service. Visit our website at www.hoddereducation.co.uk

© Moira Brown 2015
First published in 2015 by
Hodder Education,
An Hachette UK Company
338 Euston Road
London NW1 3BH

Impression number   10 9 8 7 6 5 4 3 2 1
Year   2019 2018 2017 2016 2015

Cover illustration by Sandy Lightley
Illustrations by Marleen Visser
Typeset in Swissforall 14pt
Printed in Great Britain by Hobbs the Printers, Totton, Hampshire

A catalogue record for this title is available from the British Library

ISBN 978 1471 830235